Far and Few

far and few

Rhymes of the Never Was and Always Is

by David McCord

DRAWINGS BY HENRY B. KANE

Little, Brown and Company · *Boston*

LIBRARY OF CONGRESS CATALOG CARD NO. 52–8336

Seventh Printing

A few of these poems have appeared before in print and I have
thank the following publishers and editors: Charles Scribner's So
for four poems from *The Crows* by David McCord (copyright 19
by Charles Scribner's Sons); Doubleday & Co., Inc. for one poe
from *A Star by Day* (copyright 1950, by David McCord) and f
five lines from *The Camp at Lockjaw* (copyright 1952, by Dav
McCord); Coward-McCann, Inc. for one poem from *And Wha
More* (copyright 1941, by David McCord); Harcourt, Brace & C
Inc. for three poems from *Rainbow in the Sky* edited by Louis Unte
meyer (copyright 1935 by Harcourt, Brace & Co., Inc.); *The Satu
day Review of Literature; The New Yorker* (the poem "Cocoo
was copyrighted in 1949 by The New Yorker Magazine, Inc., und
the title of "Sing Cocoon"); *Ladies' Home Journal; The Atlan
Monthly* and *The Boston Globe.*   D. T. W. McC.

*Printed simultaneously
in Canada by McClelland and Stewart Limited*

PRINTED IN THE UNITED STATES OF AMERICA

For
E · B · R · McC
over all the years

"Not the less revere the Giver,
Leave the many and hold the few."

Father and I in the Woods

"Son,"
My father used to say,
"Don't run."

"Walk,"
My father used to say,
"Don't talk."

"Words,"
My father used to say,
"Scare birds."

So be:
It's sky and brook and bird
And tree.

Contents

Far and Few

Joe

We feed the birds in winter,
And outside in the snow
We have a tray of many seeds
For many birds of many breeds
And one gray squirrel named Joe.
        But Joe comes early,
        Joe comes late,
        And all the birds
        Must stand and wait.
And waiting there for Joe to go
Is pretty cold work in the snow.

Five Little Bats

Five little bats flew out of the attic:
Five little bats all acrobatic.

One little bat flew through the city,
One little bat was flitting pretty.

One little bat flew round the gable,
One little bat was not flight able.

One little bat flew in and out of
Something or other, I haven't a doubt of

That, or that five little bats erratic
Flew back in and are now up attic.

Five Chants

I

Every time I climb a tree
Every time I climb a tree
Every time I climb a tree
I scrape a leg
Or skin a knee
And every time I climb a tree
I find some ants
Or dodge a bee
And get the ants
All over me

And every time I climb a tree
Where have you been?
They say to me
But don't they know that I am free
Every time I climb a tree?
I like it best
To spot a nest
That has an egg
Or maybe three

And then I skin
The other leg
But every time I climb a tree
I see a lot of things to see
Swallows rooftops and TV
And all the fields and farms there be
Every time I climb a tree
Though climbing may be good for ants
It isn't awfully good for pants
But still it's pretty good for me
Every time I climb a tree

II

Monday morning back to school
Fool fool fool fool
Monday morning back we go
No No No No
Monday morning summer's gone
John John John John
Monday morning what a pain
Jane Jane Jane Jane

III

The pickety fence
The pickety fence
Give it a lick it's
The pickety fence
Give it a lick it's
A clickety fence
Give it a lick it's
A lickety fence
Give it a lick
Give it a lick
Give it a lick
With a rickety stick
Pickety
Pickety
Pickety
Pick

IV

The cow has a cud
The turtle has mud
The rabbit has a hutch
But I haven't much

The ox has a yoke
The frog has a croak
The toad has a wart
So he's not my sort

The mouse has a hole
The polecat a pole
The goose has a hiss
And it goes like this

The duck has a pond
The bird has beyond
The hen has a chick
But I feel sick

The horse has hay
The dog has his day
The bee has a sting
And a queen not a king

The robin has a worm
The worm has a squirm
The squirrel has a nut
Every wheel has a rut

The pig has a pen
The bear has a den
The trout has a pool
While I have school

The crow has a nest
The hawk has a quest
The owl has a mate
Doggone! I'm late!

V

Thin ice
Free advice
Heavy snow
Out you go
Nice slush
Lush lush
Wet feet
Fever heat
Stuffy head
Stay in bed
Who's ill?
Me? A pill?

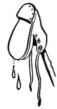

The Rainbow

The rainbow arches in the sky,
But in the earth it ends;
And if you ask the reason why,
They'll tell you "That depends."

It never comes without the rain,
Nor goes without the sun;
And though you try with might and main,
You'll never catch me one.

Perhaps you'll see it once a year,
Perhaps you'll say: "No, twice";
But every time it does appear,
It's very clean and nice.

If I were God, I'd like to win
At sun-and-moon croquet:
I'd drive the rainbow-wickets in
And ask someone to play.

The Star in the Pail

I took the pail for water when the sun was high
And left it in the shadow of the barn nearby.

When evening slippered over like the moth's brown wing,
I went to fetch the water from the cool wellspring.

The night was clear and warm and wide, and I alone
Was walking by the light of stars as thickly sown

As wheat across the prairie, or the first fall flakes,
Or spray upon the lawn — the kind the sprinkler makes.

But every star was far away as far can be,
With all the starry silence sliding over me.

And every time I stopped I set the pail down slow,
For when I stooped to pick the handle up to go

Of all the stars in heaven there was one to spare,
And he silvered in the water and I left him there.

At the Garden Gate

Who so late
At the garden gate?
Emily, Kate,
And John.
"*John*,
Where have you been?
It's after six;
Supper is on,
And you've been gone
An hour,
John!"
"We've been, we've been,
We've just been over
The field," said
John.
(Emily, Kate,
And John.)

Who so late
At the garden gate?
Emily, Kate,
And John.
"John,
What have you got?"
"A whopping toad.
Isn't he big?
He's a terrible
Load.

(We found him
A little ways
Up the road,"
Said Emily,
Kate,
And John.)

Who so late
At the garden gate?
Emily, Kate,
And John.
"*John,
Put that thing down!*
Do you want to get warts?"
(They all three have 'em
By last
Reports.)
Still, finding toads
Is the best of
Sports,
Say Emily,
Kate,
And John.

The Fisherman

The little boy is fishing
With a green fishline,
And he has got me wishing
That his line were mine.

The little boy is fishing
With a fresh-cut pole,
And he has got me wishing
For his fishing hole.

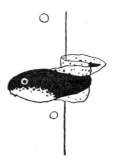

The little boy is fishing
With better than a pin,
And he has got me wishing
That he won't fall in.

The little boy is fishing
With a disenchanted slug,
And he has got me wishing
For the first faint tug.

The little boy is fishing
With a cider-cork float,
And he has got me wishing
For the cider and a boat.

The little boy is fishing
For I don't know what,
And he has got my wishing
In an awful knot.

Something Better

We have a nice clean new green lawn,
And that's the one I'm playing on.
But down the street a little piece
There is a man who has three geese.
And when you see them, just beyond
You'll see a nice new deep blue pond.

The Newt

The little newt
Is not a brute,
A fish or fowl,
A kind of owl:
He doesn't prowl
Or run or dig
Or grow too big.
He doesn't fly
Or laugh or cry —
He doesn't try.

The little newt
Is mostly mute,
And grave and wise,
And has two eyes.
He lives inside,
Or likes to hide;
But after rain
He's out again
And rather red,
I should have said.

The little newt
Of great repute
Has legs, a tail,
A spotted veil.
He walks alone
From stone to stone,

From log to log,
From bog to bog,
From tree to tree,
From you to me.

The little newt
By grass or root
Is very kind
But hard to find.
His hands and feet
Are always neat:
They move across
The mildest moss.
He's very shy,
He's never spry —
Don't ask me why.

Dividing

Here is an apple, ripe and red
  On one side; on the other green.
And I must cut it with a knife
  Across or in between.

And if I cut it in between,
  And give the best (as Mother said)
To you, then I must keep the green,
  And you will have the red.

But Mother says that green is tough
  Unless it comes in applesauce.
You *know* what? I've been sick enough:
  I'll cut it straight across.

23

The Frost Pane

What's the good of breathing
On the window
Pane
In summer?
You can't make a frost
On the window pane
In summer.
You can't write a
Nalphabet,
You can't draw a
Nelephant;

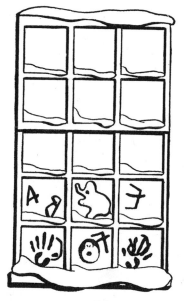

You can't make a smudge
With your nose
In summer.

Lots of good, breathing
On the window
Pane
In winter.
You can make a frost
On the window pane
In winter.
A white frost, a light frost,
A thick frost, a quick frost,
A write-me-out-a-picture-frost
Across the pane
In winter.

The Grasshopper

Down
a
deep
well
a
grasshopper
fell.

By kicking about
He thought to get out.
        He might have known better,
        For that got him wetter.
To kick round and round
Is the way to get drowned,
        And drowning is what
        I should tell you he got.

But
the
well
had
a
rope
that
dangled
some
hope.

And sure as molasses
On one of his passes
    He found the rope handy
    And up he went, *and he*

it
up
and
it
up
and
it
up
and
it
up
went

And hopped away proper
As any grasshopper.

The Hunter

The tiny young hunter arose with the morn.
He took up his gun and his powder horn,
And hied him away for the fields of the sun
With his wee powder horn and his minikin gun.

The tiny young hunter looked into the wood
That frowned on the fields of the sun where he stood;
He shot him a fox and a rabbit and one
Silinikin bear with his minikin gun.

Far, far from his wood by the fields of the sun,
With his wee powder horn and his minikin gun,
The tiny young hunter returned to his bed
And dreamed he went hunting again (so he said).

Tiger Lily

The tiger lily is a panther,
Orange to black spot:
Her tongue is the velvet pretty anther,
And she's in the vacant lot.

The cool day lilies grow beside her,
But they are done now and dead,
And between them a little silver spider
Hangs from a thread.

The Firetender

Each morning when the dawn returns,
And hills and trees and fields and ferns
Are grateful in the gaining light,
He rises from the dead of night
And rakes the star-coals up the sky
Until the flames burn bright and high,
And every cloud that eastward is
Is reddened by that fire of his.

At evening when the day is done,
And comes an end of play and fun,
The old Firetender lifts his rake —
He gives the sky a mighty shake,
And down the west the star-coals roll,
To scatter in the western bowl.
He watches the reflection spread,
Then banks the fire and goes to bed.

Notice

I have a dog,
I had a cat.
I've got a frog
Inside my hat.

Rhyme

The bee thrives
on honey and hives,
the cat apparently
has nine lives,
Bluebeard was difficult
for wives,
and some day I shall count
by fives.

The Door

Why is there more
behind a door
than there is
before:
Kings,
things
in store:
faces,
places
to explore:
The marvelous shore,
the rolling floor,
the green man
by the sycamore?

This Is My Rock

This is my rock,
And here I run
To steal the secret of the sun;

This is my rock,
And here come I
Before the night has swept the sky;

This is my rock,
This is the place
I meet the evening face to face.

Tiggady Rue

Curious, curious Tiggady Rue
Looks and looks in the heart of you;
She finds you good,
She finds you bad,
Generous, mean,
Grumpy, glad —
Tiggady Rue.

Curious, curious Tiggady Rue
Tells your thoughts and tells you *you;*
Elephant thoughts,
And spry and lean,
And thoughts made like a jumping bean,
Or wedgy ones
Slid in between —
She knows them, too,
If she looks at you,
Tiggady Rue.

Curious, curious Tiggady Rue
Knows your thoughts and you and you.
When dusk is down
On field and town,
Beware!
Take care!
If she looks at you —
Tiggady Rue.

All About Fireflies All About

The stars are all so far away
For creature-kind that hide by day
(For moth and mouse and toad and such)
The starlight doesn't count for much.
And that is why a field at night
In May or June is plaintive, bright
With little lanterns sailing by,
Like stars across a mimic sky,
Just high enough — but not too high.

Compass Song

North, south, east, and west,
Summer, spring, winter, fall:
Each of you I love the best,
All of you — *all*.

Summernorth, wintersouth,
Eastfall and westspring:
Clapper in the big bell mouth,
Ring the bell — *ring!*

From the Mailboat Passing By

In the long lake's mirror
Everything is upside down.
But nothing could be clearer:
Mountain, bridge, and town;
  Pine tree, birch, and oak,
   Tall smoke,
  All topside upside down:
   Even the fisherfolk,
   Even a smile or frown.

Tomorrows

Tomorrows never seem to stay,
Tomorrow will be yesterday
Before you know.
Tomorrows have a sorry way
Of turning into just today,
And so . . . and so . . .

In the Middle

I think about the elephant and flea,
For somewhere in between them there is me.

Perhaps the flea is unaware of this:
Perhaps I'm not what elephants would miss.

I don't know how the flea puts in his day;
I guess an elephant just likes to sway.

But there they are: one little and one large,
And in between them only me in charge!

45

Mr. Macklin's Jack o'Lantern

Mr. Macklin takes his knife
And carves the yellow pumpkin face:
Three holes bring eyes and nose to life,
The mouth has thirteen teeth in place.

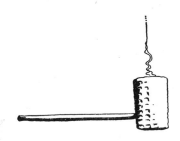

Then Mr. Macklin just for fun
Transfers the corn-cob pipe from his
Wry mouth to Jack's, and everyone
Dies laughing! O what fun it is

Till Mr. Macklin draws the shade
And lights the candle in Jack's skull.
Then all the inside dark is made
As spooky and as horrorful

As Halloween, and creepy crawl
The shadows on the tool-house floor,
With Jack's face dancing on the wall.
O Mr. Macklin! Where's the door?

Snail

This sticky trail
Was made by snail.
Snail makes no track
That he'll take back.
However slow,
His word is go.
(Twixt me and you
The word is goo.)

The Starfish

When I see a starfish
Upon the shining sand,
I ask him how he liked the sea
And if he likes the land.
"Would you rather be a starfish
Or an out-beyond-the-bar fish?"
I whisper very softly,
And he seems to understand.

He never *says* directly,
But I fancy all the same
That he knows the answer quite as well
As if it were his name:
"An out-beyond-the-bar fish
Is much happier than a starfish";
And when I look for him again
He's gone the way he came.

Cocoon

The little caterpillar creeps
Awhile before in silk it sleeps.
It sleeps awhile before it flies,
And flies awhile before it dies,
And that's the end of three good tries.

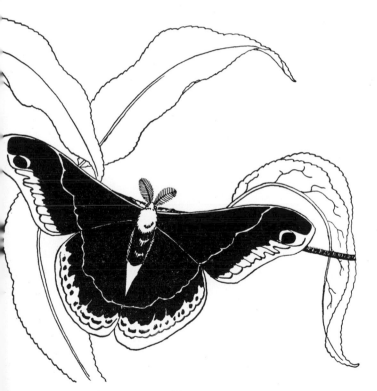

Waltzing Mice

Every night as I go to bed
I think of the prayer I should have said;
And even now as I bow my head:
"Please, O Lord, may I have instead
Some waltzing mice, a gun, and a sled?"

I don't suppose they're much of a price,
But Uncle Ted (without advice)
Gave me skates, and there isn't ice;
And I could have been saying, "How terribly *nice*,
A gun, a sled, and waltzing mice!"

Every night when play is done,
I think them all over, one by one;
"And quite the splendidest, Lord, for fun
Are waltzing mice, a sled, and a gun."

Smart Mr. Doppler

Smart Mr. Doppler
Was a queer sort of bird,
Not for things he did
But for sounds he heard.
Well, the sounds he heard
Are the sounds we hear,
But this Mr. Doppler
Had the better ear,
And this Mr. Doppler
Had the brighter mind;
So today one sound is the Doppler kind.

Hearing all the clamor
Of an engine bell,
He knew that it was coming
If it seemed to swell:
clang CLANG CLANG CLANG CLANG
             (it rang)
CLANG CLANG CLANG CLANG *clang*.

And that was another very odd thing too:
The pitch went down when the sound passed through:
        clang
        CLANG
        CLANG
        CLANG
        CLANG

(past you)
CLANG
CLANG
CLANG
CLANG
clang.

Smart Mr. Doppler
Is long since gone:
But you can hear him everywhere
From dark to dawn.
From dawn to dark
You can hear him:
HARK!

Riding on the train
When another goes by,
With the bell ding . . . *dong* . . . ding . .
higher, HIGHER, HIGH;
With the ding-dong-dang of it, . .
LOWER, LOWER, *low*. . . .

When you hear it so
You will always know
That smart Mr. Doppler
Is still on the go!

Owls Talking

I think that many owls say *Who-o:*
At least the owls that I know do-o.
But somewhere when some owls do not-t,
Perhaps they cry *Which-h*, *Why-y*, or *What-t*.

Or when they itch-h
They just say *Which-h*,
Or close one eye-e
And try *What-t Why-y*.

Far Away

How far, today,
Is far away?
It's farther now than I can say,
It's farther now than you can say,
It's farther now than who can say,
It's very *very* far away:
You'd better better better play,
You'd better stay and play today.
Okay . . . okay . . . okay.

The Shell

I took away the ocean once,
Spiraled in a shell,
And happily for months and months
I heard it very well.

How is it then that I should hear
What months and months before
Had blown upon me sad and clear,
Down by the grainy shore?

Watching the Moon

September evenings such as these
The moon hides early in the trees,
And when we drive along the shore
I think I miss the trees the more
Because the moon is coming down
Beyond the branches and will drown.

Asleep and Awake

Nothing in the sky is high,
Nothing in the sea is deep,
Nothing on the street goes by
When I'm asleep.

Nothing but the world is wide,
Nothing but a storm can break,
Nothing but a star can hide
When I'm awake.

The White Ships

Out from the beach the ships I see
On cloudy sails move sleepily,
And though the wind be fair and strong
I watch them steal like ants along,
Following free, or wheeling now
To dip the sun a golden prow.

But when I ride upon the train
And turn to find the ships again,
I catch them far against the sky,
With crowded canvas hurrying by,
To all intent as fast as we
Are thundering beside the sea.

At Low Tide

A broken saucer of the sea
Is lying on the sand,
With seaweed like the leaves of tea,
Brown as the boy's brown hand —

The small brown boy with pail and spade,
The connoisseur of kelp,
Considering what the tide has made
And best how he can help.

The Wind

Wind in the garden,
Wind on the hill,
Wind I-am-blowing,
Never be still.

Wind I-am-blowing,
I love you the best:
Out of the morning,
Into the west.

Out of the morning,
Washed in the blue,
Wind I-am-blowing,
Where are you?

Our Mr. Toad

Our Mr. Toad
Has a nice abode
Under the first front step.
When it rains he's cool
In a secret pool
Where the water goes
    drip
    drop
    drep.

Our Mr. Toad
Will avoid the road:
He's a private-cellar man.
And it's not much fun
In the broiling sun
When you *have* a good
    ten
    tone
    tan.

Our Mr. Toad
Has a kind of code
That tells him the coast is clear.
Then away he'll hop
With a stop, stop, stop
When the dusk draws
    nigh
    no
    near.

Fat Father Robin

Fat father robin,
A red rubber ball,
Rolls across the lawn
And bounces off the wall.

Rolls, bounces, rolls away,
Hearing in the ground
The worm talking tunnel
And the mole saying mound.

August 28

A flock of swallows have gone flying south;
The bluejay carries acorns in his mouth.
I don't know where he carries them or why.
I'm never sure I like the bluejay's cry,
But still I like his blue shape in the sky.

John

John comes in with a basket:
John is a neighborly man.
I have a question — I ask it:
John, can I mix the bran
And make the mash
With a splash in the pan
And feed the pig —
Not the awfully big
One — the little one. **Can
I, John?**

John comes in with a basket:
The basket is full of wood.
I have a question — I ask it:
John, if I'm awfully good,
Could I help today
With the hay? If I should,

I'd like to rake
While the others make.
I'd be good. Now could
I, John?

John comes in with a basket:
The basket is full of flowers.
I have a question — I ask it:
John, if it rains or showers
How would it seem
To your team of plowers
To follow for worms
With attracting squirms
And fish for hours,
Hey, John?

John comes in with a basket:
The basket is full of fruit.
I have a question — I ask it:
John, would you like to shoot
With the Indian bow

Of a Crow or a Ute —
And arrows too,
If we find a few?
We could look. Would it suit
You, John?

John comes in with a basket:
The basket is full of peas.
I have a question — I ask it:
John, if it blows a breeze,
Why couldn't we — well,
If I shelled all these —
Go fly my kite
To a flyable height
Where there aren't any trees,
Eh, John?

John comes in with a basket:
The basket that has no lid.

I have a question — I ask it:
John, there's a hen that's hid
Her nest in the loft
Where I've often slid,
But I've messed it some.
Do you think she'll come
To sit where she did
Sit, John?

John comes in with a basket:
A basket that's empty, too.
I have a question — I ask it:
John, did you know I knew?
Tomorrow we'll pack
And go back. It's true.
Do you mind to stay
With the snow and the sleigh?
I'll miss you. Will you
Me, John?

Lost

I have a little turtle
Name of Myrtle.
I have an extra lizard
Name of Wizard.
I have two kinds of snake:
Bill and Blake.
I have a dandy hutch
Without the rabbit.
If you see any such,
Will you please grab it?

Durenda Fair

Shapely, sharp Durenda Fair
Wore three roses in her hair:
One for love and one for grace
And one for any time and place.

Crows

I like to walk
And hear the black crows talk.

I like to lie
And watch crows sail the sky.

I like the crow
That wants the wind to blow:

I like the one
That thinks the wind is fun.

I like to see
Crows spilling from a tree,

And try to find
The top crow left behind.

I like to hear
Crows caw that spring is near.

I like the great
Wild clamor of crow hate

Three farms away
When owls are out by day.

I like the slow
Tired homeward-flying crow;

I like the sight
Of crows for my good night.

Who Wants a Birthday?

Who wants a birthday?
Somebody does.

"I *am*," says a birthday,
But never "I *was*."

"Five, six," says a birthday:
"You're seven!" "You're nine!"

"I'm yours," says a birthday,
"And you, child, are mine."

"*How* old?" says a birthday.
(You have to guess right.)

"You're *what?*" says a birthday.
(You may be: you *might*.)

"A cake," says a birthday,
"I'm sure there's a cake!"

"A wish," says a birthday.
"What wish do you make?"

"I'm glad," says a birthday,
"To see how you've grown."

"Hello!" says a birthday.
("Hello!" says my own.)

Isabel Jones & Curabel Lee

Isabel Jones & Curabel Lee
Lived on butter and bread and tea,
And as to that they would both agree:
Isabel, Curabel, Jones & Lee.

Isabel said: While prunes have stones
They aren't a promising food for Jones;
Curabel said: Well, as for me,
Tripe is a terrible thing for Lee.

There's not a dish of fowl or fish
For which we wish, said I. & C.
And that is why until we die
We'll eat no pie, nor beg nor buy
But butter and bread and a trace of tea.
(Signed) *Isabel Jones & Curabel Lee.*

Song Before Supper

Now everything is ready, child, and ready I'm for you,
With supper on the table and a rice-and-radish stew.
And I am even readier to find you ready too,
But all I hear you answer is a
            Ding-Dang-Dongeroo.

I know you aren't a fireman, and you say you're not a cow
I think you aren't a cowboy, but I don't know why or how
And if you're not a lion in the zoo, what *are* you now?
And *is* it Ding-Dang-Dongeroo or
            Ding-Dang-Dongerow?

You say a thousand other things that I don't understand:
They sound like frogs in water jugs or wind across the san
I don't know why you say them, but I wish you'd chang
                    your bran
So Ding-Dang-Dongeroo to you!
            Go wash your other hand!

Perhaps you're just a bicycle, a bittern in the mire,
The hook-and-ladder taking corners flying to a fire,
Lost sheep, or buoys after dark. . . . But won't you *ever* ti
Of Ding-Dang-Dongeroo, young man?
            I do. Sit up, now, *higher!*

I have it! It's a kangaroo! How did I ever miss?
A kangaroo in dungarees! But even so, no bliss
For me to listen all day long to your small orifice
Repeating Ding-Dang-Dongaroo.

                Ding-Dang! *Eat some of this!*

Through the Window

The bells are ringing for church this morning,
For church this morning the bells are rung;
And up in the loft the choir is singing,
The choir is singing, the song is sung.

The bells are ringing for church this morning,
A little boy in the seventh pew
Is listening hard to a golden warning:
A bird, perhaps, with a *Where are you?*

V

V
cry the geese
fly V
who me?
rues a goose
no use
for me
to fly a V
I'm only one of three
and three must all agree
if three will make a V
acute or obtuse
with two in the caboose
and one in the
a-po-gee

Song of the Train

Clickety-clack,
Wheels on the track,
This is the way
They begin the attack:
Click-ety-clack,
Click-ety-clack,
Click-ety, *clack*-ety,
Click-ety
Clack.

Clickety-clack,
Over the crack,
Faster and faster
The song of the track:
Clickety-clack,
Clickety-clack,
Clickety, clackety,
Clackety
Clack.

Riding in front,
Riding in back,
Everyone hears
The song of the track:
Clickety-clack,
Clickety-clack,
Clickety, *clickety*,
Clackety
Clack.

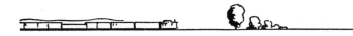

Trick or Treat

Halloween,
Halloween,
Halloween!

Latch the latch,
Catch the catch,
Scratch the match.

Witches ride,
Jack will hide
Lantern-eyed.

Better bake.
Better make
Candy, cake.

Mask or sheet:
Trick or treat!
Ghosts are fleet.

Soon or late
Sure as fate
Goes the gate.

Knocker, bell
Cast the spell.
Treat them well!

Silly sooth:
Youth is youth,
Tongue and tooth.

Treat them quick,
Else the trick:
Take your pick!

Conversation

"Mother, may I stay up tonight?"
"No, dear."
"Oh dear! (She always says 'No, dear').
But Father said I might."
"No, dear."
"He did, that is, if you thought it right."
"No, dear, it isn't right."
"Oh dear! Can I keep on the light?"
"No, dear. In spite
Of what your Father said,
You go to bed,
And in the morning you'll be bright
And glad instead
For one more day ahead."
"I might,
But not for one more night."
"No, dear — *no,* dear."
"At least I've been polite, I guess."
"Yes, dear, you've been polite —
Good night."
"Oh dear,
I'd rather stay down here —
I'm quite . . ."
"No, dear. Now, out of sight."
("Well that was pretty near — ")
"*Good* night."
(" — all right.")
"Good *night!*"

X & Y

Y is a chesty letter,
X is an active one.
Y couldn't stand up better,
X seems to walk or run.
Y is for youth, and youthful
X in his excellent way
Is pleasant. And yet to be truthful,
Child, there will come a day
When, learn as you must, the sequel —
For life has the will to vex —
Nothing for trouble will equal
Your Y and your XY and X.

Z

When all is zed and done,
Z is the letter one.
No other one for me
So lovely as a Z.

Song

Wind and wave and star and sea,
And life is O! a song for me.
Wave and wind and sea and star,
Now I shall tell them what we are.
Star and sea and wind and wave,
I am a giant, strong and brave.
Sea and star and wave and wind,
You are the tiger I have skinned.

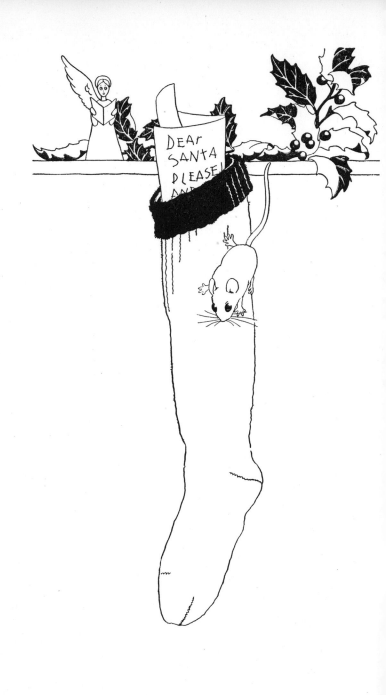

Christmas Eve

I see some waits awaiting,
I hear some singers sing.
Bell-ringers all keep ringing,
But what will Christmas bring?

The air is keen for carols;
My ears are cold, and sting.
Let Peace abide! It's hot inside,
But what will Christmas bring?

I've found a stack of stockings,
An angel with one wing.
By candlelight I've said good night,
But what will Christmas bring?

Noël, Noël! Forever
That bell-like sound a-swing
Is God and love. *I'm* thinking of:
But what will Christmas bring?

Fred

Speaking of Joe, I should have said
Our flying squirrel's name is Fred.

Fred is no flyer, but a glider.
His skin is loose and soft as eider.

But Fred himself is no softy:
He likes tough trees, and likes them lofty.

Fred is not around much at noon;
But at night, and under a bright full moon,

He sails from tree to tree like a circus performer;
And once last summer he sailed right into the dormer

Window of the empty house next door.
But that's Fred all over. Need I say more?